WHERE ARE MY HOMIES AT?

ILLUSTRATIONS BY ALEX LEHOURS

MEET THE CLIQUE

WHAT'S UP LITTLE HOMIES,

ARE YOU READY TO TAKE YOUR STREET CRED TO THE NEXT LEVEL? YOU CAN COME BE PART OF MY CLIQUE; ALL YOU HAVE TO DO IS FIND ME!

I HAVE A FEW OF MY HOMIES COMING ALONG FOR THE RIDE; CAN YOU FIND THEM? SNOOP DOGG, JAY-Z, BEYONCÉ, THE NOTORIOUS B.I.G. AND TUPAC ARE ALL IN THE HOUSE! MAKE SURE YOU FIND THE WHOLE CREW IN EVERY SCENE – REAL HOMIES DON'T LEAVE ANYONE BEHIND. YOU WILL SEE SOME MORE FAMILIAR FACES ALONG THE WAY IF YOU LOOK CLOSELY ENOUGH. I HAVE DROPPED A CHECKLIST IN THE BACK IF YOU'RE UP FOR THE CHALLENGE! BUT HOLD UP, SOMEONE HAS JACKED MY STUFF! AT EACH DESTINATION I'LL NEED YOUR HELP TO FIND MY SNEAKERS, NOTEBOOK, MICROPHONE, HAT, BACKPACK, SPRAY CAN, BASKETBALL AND MY TRUSTY WALKMAN.

THERE'S NO TIME TO WASTE! KEEP YA HEAD UP AND GET STEPPIN'!

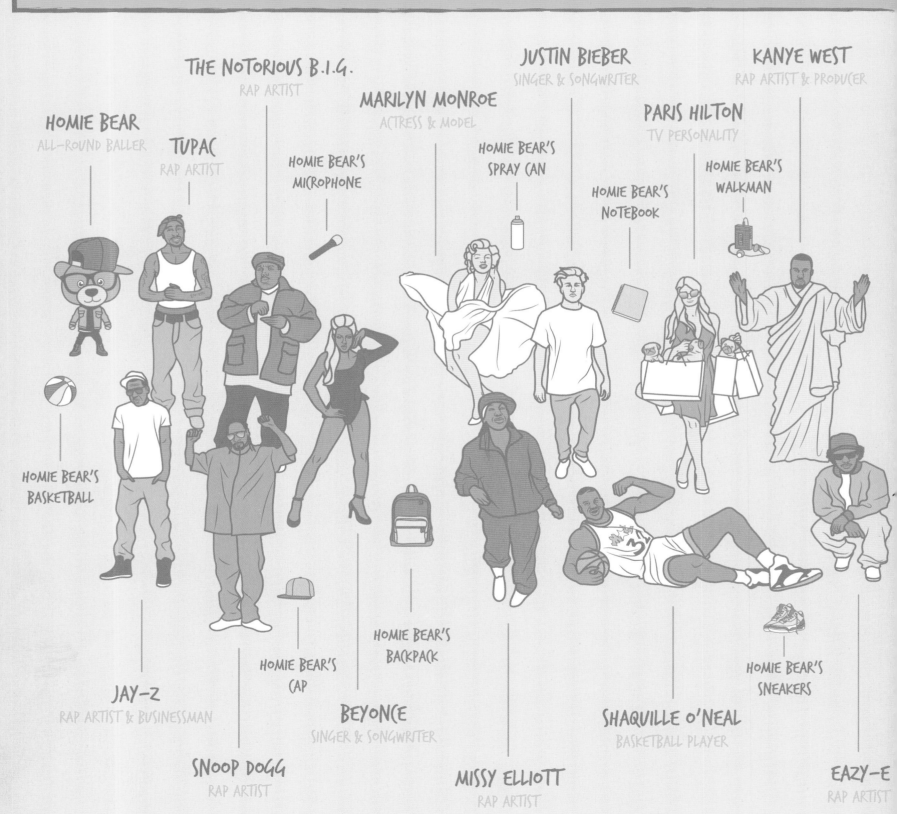

THE NOTORIOUS B.I.G.
RAP ARTIST

JUSTIN BIEBER
SINGER & SONGWRITER

KANYE WEST
RAP ARTIST & PRODUCER

MARILYN MONROE
ACTRESS & MODEL

HOMIE BEAR
ALL-ROUND BALLER

TUPAC
RAP ARTIST

HOMIE BEAR'S MICROPHONE

PARIS HILTON
TV PERSONALITY

HOMIE BEAR'S SPRAY CAN

HOMIE BEAR'S NOTEBOOK

HOMIE BEAR'S WALKMAN

HOMIE BEAR'S BASKETBALL

JAY-Z
RAP ARTIST & BUSINESSMAN

HOMIE BEAR'S CAP

HOMIE BEAR'S BACKPACK

HOMIE BEAR'S SNEAKERS

SNOOP DOGG
RAP ARTIST

BEYONCE
SINGER & SONGWRITER

MISSY ELLIOTT
RAP ARTIST

SHAQUILLE O'NEAL
BASKETBALL PLAYER

EAZY-E
RAP ARTIST

KIM JONG-UN
SUPREME LEADER OF NORTH KOREA

MICHAEL JACKSON
SINGER, SONGWRITER & DANCER

AMY WINEHOUSE
SINGER & SONGWRITER

FRIDA KAHLO
ARTIST

ALBERT EINSTEIN
THEORETICAL PHYSICIST

TOM BRADY
NFL QUARTERBACK

LENNY KRAVITZ
SINGER & SONGWRITER

CARDI B
RAP ARTIST

NICKI MINAJ
RAP ARTIST

POPE FRANCIS
266TH POPE

BARACK OBAMA
POLITICIAN

DRAKE
RAP ARTIST

KIM KARDASHIAN WEST
TV PERSONALITY

I GET AROUND

Before you get started, here's a run down of all the hotspots the crew likes to hang. From Puffy's White Party to Fight Night in Las Vegas, finishing up Sky High with all the Holy Homies that left us too soon; there is a dirty dozen to get through so what are you waiting for? You have only got one shot little homies, one opportunity. Are you going to capture it, or let it slip?

ABOVE THE RIM

FESTIVAL FEVER

WHITE HOT

HIT 'EM UP

LIGHTS! CAMERA! ACTION!

THE AWARD GOES TO

PARADISE DREAMING

HIP HOP HOORAY

COTTON CANDY CHAOS

DROP THE MIC

HOLY HOMIES

I LOVE IT PIER

FESTIVAL FEVER

WHAT UP COACHELLA? WHEN MY HOMIES SNOOP AND DRE GOT TUPAC BACK ON STAGE IT WAS LIT! NOTHING GETS ME MORE PUMPED THAN LISTENING TO SOME DOPE BEATS WITH MY CREW. CAN'T MISS #BEYCHELLA! HER PERFORMANCE IS SET TO BE FLAWLESS; PREPARE TO BOW DOWN HOMIES.

PARADISE DREAMING

A

NOW THIS IS THE REAL GANGSTA'S PARADISE. WHEN I NEED TO UNWIND, THIS IS THE PLACE TO BE. SUN, SAND, BBQS AND BEATS; ALL THIS LITTLE HOMIE NEEDS. ONCE MY CREW KNOW I'M HEADING HERE THEY ARE NEVER FAR BEHIND ME – AT LEAST COOLIO GOT THE ISLAND DRESS MEMO. IT'S GETTING HOT IN HERE!

HIP HOP HOORAY

B

IT'S TIME TO THROW YOUR HANDS IN THE AIR LIKE YOU JUST DON'T CARE! THIS IS GOING TO BE THE BIGGEST BLOCK PARTY THIS CITY HAS EVER SEEN. AIN'T NOTHING BUT A LITTLE HOMIE PARTY! WORD ON THE STREET IS MY GIRL JENNY FROM THE BLOCK IS HERE; DON'T BE FOOLED BY THE ROCKS THAT SHE'S GOT.

COTTON CANDY CHAOS

WHEN WE HIT DISNEYLAND, WE LIKE TO KICK IT BY THE TEACUPS AND THROW OUR HANDS UP ON SPLASH MOUNTAIN. THE MAIN PARADE IS POPPIN' TODAY; I LOVE SEEING MY FAVORITES BREAK IT DOWN TO A TUNE! DRIZZY SHOULD BE HERE SOON, SO I BETTER LISTEN OUT FOR THAT HOTLINE BLING.

DROP THE MIC

I'VE LOST COUNT THE NUMBER OF HOURS WE HAVE SPENT AMONGST THESE WALLS; THIS IS WHERE THE MAGIC HAPPENS! WHERE RHYMES ARE WRITTEN AND BEATS ARE DROPPED. MY CREW AND I ARE HERE ALL NIGHT TO MAKE SURE ONLY THE FRESHEST TUNES MAKE IT ON THE MIXTAPE. ARE YOU READY TO GET TO WORK?

WHITE HOT

B WHEN PUFFY INVITES YOU TO HIS WHITE PARTY, YOU STOP, COLLABORATE AND LISTEN FOR THE DETAILS — I'M GOING HAM TONIGHT HOMIES! HAIRCUT: CHECK. OUTFIT: CHECK. UBER: CHECK. NOW ALL THAT'S LEFT TO DO IS PARTY LIKE A ROCKSTAR. WHAT HAPPENS AT PUFFY'S PARTY, STAYS AT PUFFY'S PARTY — GOT IT?

LIGHTS! CAMERA! ACTION!

I LOVE BEING ON SET – SO MANY FAMOUS FACES, IT'S HARD NOT TO GET A LITTLE SHOOK. FROM MY MAN BLACK PANTHER TO MILEY SHOWING US HOW IT'S DONE ON THE WRECKING BALL; I SEE YOU BABY! ALL THESE LEGIT TALENTS MAKES ME WANT TO HEAD TO THE HILLS, THE HOLLYWOOD HILLS.

THE AWARD GOES TO

THE RED CARPET IS ALL ROLLED OUT – GOTTA MAKE SURE MY OUTFIT IS ON FLEEK BECAUSE EVERY REPORTER IS HERE READY TO POUNCE. I HOPE KIM AND KANYE DON'T RUN INTO TAYLOR SWIFT; THAT'LL BE AWKS. NOW WHERE'S MY AWARD FOR MOST TALENTED LITTLE HOMIE?

I LOVE IT PIER

NOTHING BETTER THAN A HOTDOG ON A STICK AND SMASHING OUT A NEW PB ON THE BASKETBALL SHOOTER! SANTA MONICA PIER DELIVERS THE GOODS EVERY TIME; IT'S THE REAL MEANING TO CALIFORNIA LOVE; YOU FEEL ME? I HAD MY FIRST DATE WITH BAE HERE; SPARKS WERE FLYING ON THAT FERRIS WHEEL!

CHECK YOURSELF

LITTLE HOMIES, MAJOR KEY ALERT. THERE'S MORE DOPE FUN TO BE HAD, HELP ME SEARCH HIGH AND LOW FOR A FEW MORE OF MY FAMOUS FRIENDS. EVERYONE IS HERE, FROM BARACK OBAMA, TO MY GIRL CARDI B. MAKE SURE YOU PAY ATTENTION AND KEEP YOUR EYES ON THE PRIZE; LET'S SEE HOW STRONG YOUR STREET CRED REALLY IS. IT AIN'T OVER TILL THE PHAT HOMIE SINGS!

ABOVE THE RIM

1. THE GAME
2. KYLIE JENNER & TRAVIS SCOTT
3. SHAQUILLE O'NEAL
4. LEBRON JAMES
5. JUSTIN BIEBER
6. SPIDERMAN
7. THE POPE
8. OPRAH
9. STEPHEN CURRY
10. SPACE JAM CREW (6)
11. JACK NICHOLSON
12. YAO MING
13. FERGIE
14. MICHAEL JORDAN
15. SANTA CLAUS
16. KOBE BRYANT

FESTIVAL Fever

1. THE WEEKND
2. DR. DRE
3. KIM JONG-UN
4. HARRY POTTER
5. PARIS HILTON
6. BART SIMPSON
7. LENNY KRAVITZ
8. RIHANNA & CALVIN HARRIS
9. BARNEY
10. AVATAR
11. BAMBI
12. LILY ALLEN
13. BUZZ & WOODY
14. SERENA WILLIAMS
15. GERI HALLIWELL
16. KHALEESI

Paradise DREAMING

1. NELLY
2. COOLIO
3. DESTINY'S CHILD
4. PAMELA ANDERSON & THE HOFF
5. RICHARD BRANSON
6. DJ KHALED
7. WIL.I.AM
8. KELLY SLATER
9. CRISTIANO RONALDO & DAVID BECKHAM
10. T-PAIN
11. CAPTAIN HOOK
12. ELLEN DEGENERES & PORTIA DE ROSSI
13. MAUI & MOANA
14. ARNOLD SCHWARZENEGGER
15. EINSTEIN
16. HULK HOGAN

HIP HOP ~~HOORAY~~

1. J-LO
2. EAZY-E
3. OSCAR THE GROUCH
4. MARIO & SONIC
5. MICHAEL JACKSON
6. THE ROCK
7. PIKACHU
8. MC HAMMER
9. RAPHAEL THE TMNT
10. BIG BIRD
11. MARY POPPINS
12. THE SEINFELD CREW
13. BATMAN & ROBIN
14. MISSY ELLIOTT
15. J DILLA
16. BUGS BUNNY

COTTON CANDY CHAOS

1. DRAKE
2. E.T.
3. WINNIE THE POOH
4. SNOW WHITE
5. KOURTNEY KARDASHIAN
6. ED SHEERAN
7. MICHAEL PHELPS
8. TIMON & PUMBAA
9. ALICE IN WONDERLAND
10. ARIEL
11. ELSA
12. LILO & STITCH
13. BEAUTY & THE BEAST
14. PRINCESS JASMINE
15. CINDERELLA
16. DONALD DUCK

DROP THE MIC

1. ALICIA KEYS
2. KERMIT & MISS PIGGY
3. CARDI B
4. CHRIS BROWN
5. T-PAIN
6. DR. DRE
7. BRITNEY SPEARS
8. EMINEM
9. LIL WAYNE
10. EVE
11. GENE SIMMONS
12. NAS
13. J.COLE
14. JOHN LEGEND & CHRISSY TEIGEN
15. AKON
16. NICKI MINAJ

HIT EM' UP

1. 50 CENT	9. OPTIMUS PRIME
2. ROCKY	10. NACHO LIBRE
3. MANNY PACQUIAO	11. RONDA ROUSEY
4. SCOTT 'THE LORD' DISICK	12. ZANGIEF
5. GOKU & PICCOLO	13. HARLEY QUINN
6. CONOR MCGREGOR	14. MIKE TYSON
7. FLOYD MAYWEATHER	15. IVAN DRAGO
8. THE KARATE KID & MR MIYAGI	16. MUHAMMAD ALI

WHITE HOT

1. PUFF DADDY & CASSIE	9. NSYNC
2. VANILLA ICE	10. HOMER & PETER GRIFFIN
3. ALADDIN	11. PITBULL
4. POST MALONE	12. R2D2
5. SALT BAE	13. COLONEL SANDERS
6. KENDRICK LAMAR	14. GANDALF
7. BARACK OBAMA	15. OLAF
8. CRUELLA DE VILLE	16. STEVE AOKI

LIGHTS CAMERA ACTION

1. MEN IN BLACK	9. BLACK PANTHER
2. CHEWBACCA	10. BORAT
3. ZORRO	11. JAMES BOND
4. MILEY CYRUS	12. THANOS
5. OPRAH & TOM CRUISE	13. CAPTAIN AMERICA & IRONMAN
6. CHARLIE CHAPLIN	14. NEO & MORPHEUS
7. DARTH VADER & YODA	15. FORREST GUMP
8. LARA CROFT	16. CHRIS PRATT

THE AWARD GOES TO

1. KATIE PERRY	9. BONO
2. KANYE & KIM KARDASHIAN WEST	10. ICE CUBE
3. WILL & JADA PINKETT SMITH	11. LL COOL J
4. ARIANA GRANDE	12. OUTKAST
5. TAYLOR SWIFT	13. MADONNA
6. BACKSTREET BOYS	14. PHARRELL
7. DJ KHALED & ASAHD	15. J-LO
8. LADY GAGA	16. JESSICA RABBIT

I LOVE IT ♥ PIER

1. KELIS	9. FRIDA KAHLO
2. XZIBIT	10. SNOOKI
3. MARTIN LUTHER KING JR	11. KHLOE KARDASHIAN & TRUE
4. JA RULE	12. MARIAH CAREY
5. QUEEN ELIZABETH II	13. THE TERMINATOR
6. TOM BRADY	14. ARI GOLD
7. RUN DMC	15. JAY GATSBY
8. USHER	16. MARGE SIMPSON

holy homies

1. BOB MARLEY	9. PAUL WALKER
2. ROBIN WILLIAMS	10. PROFESSOR SEVERUS SNAPE
3. JIMI HENDRIX	11. HEATH LEDGER
4. MUFASA	12. STEVE JOBS
5. WHITNEY HOUSTON	13. PRINCESS DIANA
6. LISA 'LEFT EYE' LOPES	14. EAZY-E
7. MARILYN MONROE	15. AVICII
8. AMY WINEHOUSE	16. STEVE IRWIN

WANT TO TAKE YOUR STREET CRED TO THE NEXT LEVEL? HIT UP WWW.MYHOMIEFINDER.COM FOR A CHEAT SHEET AND EXCLUSIVE SECRET SCENE!

ABOVE THE RIMO

Par...

FEST...

HIP HOP

HOORAY

DRO...

HIT EM' UP

★★ THE ★★

AWARD

GOES TO

I L...

IT P...

dise DREAMING

XAI-
fever COTTON
CANDY
CHAOS

THE
MIC WHITE HOT

TS CAMERA ACTION

VE
ER holy homies